Love and Kisses, Snoopy

Charles M. Schulz

Selected Cartoons from
SUMMERS FLY, WINTERS WALK
Volume 2

CORONET BOOKS
Hodder Fawcett, London

Copyright © 1976 United Feature Syndicate Inc.

First published by Fawcett Publications Inc., New York 1980

Coronet edition 1981

British Library C.I.P.

Schulz, Charles M.
   Love and kisses, Snoopy. – (Coronet books)
   1. American wit and humor, pictorial
   I. Title
   741.5'973   NC1429

ISBN 0 340 26801 8

Printed and bound in Great Britain for
Hodder Fawcett Ltd.,
Mill Road, Dunton Green, Sevenoaks,
Kent (Editorial Office: 47 Bedford
Square, London, WC1 3DP) by
Cox & Wyman Ltd, Reading

**Also by the same author,
and available in Coronet Books:**

PEANUTS comic strips to follow: © 1976 United Feature Syndicate, Inc.

SIR, THE KID BEHIND ME KEEPS CALLING ME NAMES...

POINT HIM OUT TO ME WHEN WE GET TO CAMP, MARCIE, AND I'LL SHORTEN HIS LIFE SPAN!

THAT'S OKAY, SIR.. I ALREADY HIT HIM...

MAYBE HE'S HURT...DO YOU HAVE A FIRST AID KIT?

THAT'S WHAT I HIT HIM WITH!

MARCIE, YOU'RE GONNA KILL THAT KID WHO'S BEEN CALLING YOU NAMES!

YOU'VE HIT HIM WITH A FIRST-AID KIT, CLOBBERED HIM WITH A LUNCH TRAY, PUSHED HIM INTO THE LAKE AND SHOVED HIM INTO A PATCH OF POISON OAK!!

HAVE YOU NOTICED, SIR, THAT HE HASN'T CALLED ME A NAME ALL DAY?

WHERE IS HE NOW?

IN THE DISPENSARY!

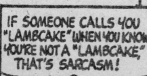

FLOYD SEEMS LIKE A NICE KID, MARCIE, AND HE REALLY LIKES YOU...

I'VE NEVER OWNED A DOG, OR A CAT, OR A HORSE, OR A HAMSTER OR ANYTHING, SIR... I'M SURE NOT READY FOR A BOY FRIEND!

YOU MEAN A GIRL HAS TO HAVE OWNED A DOG, AND A CAT, AND A HORSE AND A HAMSTER BEFORE SHE CAN HAVE A BOY FRIEND?!

EVERYTHING IN ITS TIME, SIR!

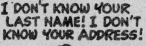

WAS "LAMBCAKE" SUCH A BAD THING TO BE CALLED, MARCIE?

WHAT ABOUT NOODLENECK OR CEMENTHEAD? PEOPLE CALL EACH OTHER LOTS OF STRANGE THINGS WITHOUT BEING REALLY SERIOUS...

YOU SHOULD THINK ABOUT THAT, MARCIE

I WILL

GOOD NIGHT, NOODLENECK!

I'M A REPORTER FOR OUR SCHOOL PAPER, CHARLIE BROWN.. CAN ANYTHING BE DONE ABOUT VIOLENCE IN SPORTS?

TELL THEM NOT TO HIT THE BALL SO HARD!

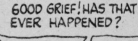

I'M WRITING AN ARTICLE FOR OUR SCHOOL PAPER ABOUT VIOLENCE IN SPORTS...

A JUDGE RECENTLY DECLARED THAT A HOCKEY STICK IS A "DANGEROUS WEAPON"... DO YOU AGREE?

IN ALL MY YEARS OF PLAYING BASEBALL, I'VE NEVER BEEN HIT WITH A HOCKEY STICK!

THAT'S ANOTHER FOR MY LIST OF STUPID ANSWERS

YOU WANNA HEAR A GOOD ONE?

I LIVE NEAR THIS SHOPPING CENTER, CHUCK, AND I SAW SOMETHING FUNNY THERE THE OTHER DAY...

THEY HAVE A BOOK STORE AND AN ICE CREAM STORE NEXT TO EACH OTHER

THE BOOK STORE HAS A SIGN IN ITS WINDOW THAT SAYS, "PLEASE DO NOT BRING ICE CREAM INTO THE BOOK STORE"

THE ICE CREAM STORE HAS A SIGN THAT SAYS, "OKAY, THEN PLEASE DON'T BRING BOOKS INTO OUR ICE CREAM STORE"

SPEAKING OF READING AND EATING, I DON'T KNOW WHY IT IS, BUT WHENEVER I TRY TO READ A BOOK AND EAT POTATO CHIPS, MY EYES ALWAYS WATER...

I HATE TALKING TO YOU, CHUCK!

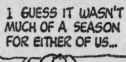

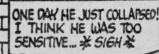

A PRIVATE SCHOOL MIGHT DO ME A LOT OF GOOD, CHUCK

I MIGHT EVEN BECOME ONE OF THE BEAUTIFUL PEOPLE! WOULDN'T THAT BE SOMETHING?

I CAN SEE YOU NOW IN A WHITE BLOUSE AND A BLUE SKIRT RUNNING OUT TO PLAY FIELD HOCKEY...

DON'T HASSLE ME WITH YOUR SARCASM, CHUCK!

THESE ARE BROCHURES FOR PRIVATE SCHOOLS MARCIE...

HERE'S ONE THAT ADVERTISES "ADVENTURE FELLOWSHIP AND CREATIVITY!" AND HERE'S ONE THAT HAS AN INDOOR RIDING RING AND AN OLYMPIC POOL!

HERE'S ONE THAT HAS FIELD TRIPS TO NORWAY AND HOLLAND!

HERE'S ONE SIR, THAT EMPHASIZES REMEDIAL READING..

ARE YOU TRYING TO BRING ME BACK DOWN TO EARTH, MARCIE?

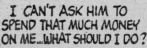

IS THIS THE "ACE OBEDIENCE SCHOOL"?

IT IS? GOOD! I'M HERE TO ENROLL! DOG? NO, MA'AM, I DIDN'T BRING A DOG...

I NOTICE THAT A LOT OF YOUR STUDENTS DO HAVE DOGS, DON'T THEY?

IS THIS ONE OF THOSE PROGRESSIVE SCHOOLS?

HOW WAS YOUR FIRST DAY AT PRIVATE SCHOOL, SIR?

WAS THE "ACE OBEDIENCE SCHOOL" ALL YOU EXPECTED?

MORE, MARCIE, A LOT MORE! THEY REALLY STRESS MANNERS AND SOCIAL GRACES...

WE SPENT THE WHOLE FIRST DAY JUST LEARNING HOW TO SIT!

THE "ACE OBEDIENCE SCHOOL" HAS CHANGED MY WHOLE LIFE, CHUCK!

REMEMBER HOW DISCOURAGED I USED TO GET ABOUT SCHOOL?

AT THE "ACE OBEDIENCE SCHOOL" THEY DON'T LET YOU GET DISCOURAGED...

EVERY TIME YOU DO SOMETHING RIGHT THEY PAT YOU ON THE HEAD!

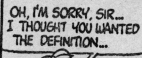

THAT'S RIGHT, CHUCK... I GRADUATED!

NO, I DON'T EVER HAVE TO GO TO SCHOOL AGAIN... I'M A CERTIFIED GRADUATE OF THE "ACE OBEDIENCE SCHOOL..."

THANKS CHUCK...WELL YOU KNOW HOW MUCH I'VE ALWAYS WANTED A GOOD EDUCATION... AND YOU KNOW WHAT I'VE ALWAYS SAID...

A GOOD EDUCATION IS THE NEXT BEST THING TO A PUSHY MOTHER!

THEY DON'T BELIEVE ME, CHUCK!

THE TEACHER AND PRINCIPAL AT SCHOOL DON'T BELIEVE I'VE GRADUATED! THEY WANT ME BACK IN SCHOOL!

I'M GONNA SHOW 'EM MY DIPLOMA FROM THE "ACE OBEDIENCE SCHOOL," BUT I THINK I SHOULD TAKE ALONG MY ATTORNEY...IS HE AROUND?

YOUR CLIENT IS ON THE WAY OVER...

"THE LIFE OF THE LAW HAS NOT BEEN LOGIC...IT HAS BEEN EXPERIENCE"

SO YOU'RE GOING TO BE PEPPERMINT PATTY'S ATTORNEY

IT SHOULD BE AN INTERESTING CASE...

ARE YOU THE DEFENSE ATTORNEY OR THE PROSECUTING ATTORNEY?

I NEVER KNOW UNTIL THE TRIAL IS OVER!

THERE'S SOMETHING I'VE ALWAYS WONDERED ABOUT...

DO YOU ATTORNEYS FIND IT VERY DIFFICULT TO PREPARE FOR A TRIAL?

THE HARDEST PART IS TRYING TO DECIDE WHAT TO PUT IN YOUR BRIEFCASE...

THE LAST TIME I WAS IN COURT I FORGOT MY HAIR SPRAY!

OKAY, ATTORNEY, LET'S GO!

THIS SHOULD BE AN EASY CASE FOR YOU... THEY'RE WRONG, AND I'M RIGHT!

I HOPE YOU DON'T MIND EASY CASES...

IF THE MONEY IS RIGHT, I CAN STAND ANYTHING, SWEETIE!

EXCUSE ME, SIR...

I DON'T KNOW WHY MY ATTORNEY IS SO ANXIOUS TO LEAVE....

ANYWAY, THAT'S MY DIPLOMA FROM THE "ACE OBEDIENCE SCHOOL," AND...

WHAT?!?

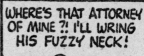

SNOOPY, OL' PAL, I OWE YOU AN APOLOGY...

THERE I WAS, ALL SET TO POUND YOU, AND YET YOU CAME TO MY RESCUE WHEN I WAS FIGHTING THAT CAT

I DIDN'T EVEN KNOW IT WAS A REAL CAT...I THOUGHT IT WAS YOU DRESSED IN A CAT SUIT!

NO WONDER HE WAS SO MAD...I KEPT TRYING TO PULL THE SUIT OVER HIS HEAD!

HEE HEE HEE HEE

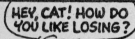

ROUND TRIP
FIRST CLASS

OCTOBER TWENTY-FOURTH

WELL ONLY ONE MORE WEEK TIL HALLOWEEN, AND THEN THE..

DON'T START IN AGAIN ABOUT THE "GREAT PUMPKIN"!

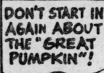

IF YOU START RAVING TO ME AGAIN ABOUT THE "GREAT PUMPKIN," I'LL POUND YOU CLEAR ACROSS THE ROOM!

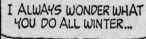

MY GRANDMOTHER LOVED TO DANCE

EVERY SATURDAY NIGHT SHE AND HER FRIENDS WENT TO THIS LITTLE PLACE THAT HAD A JUKE BOX, AND A DANCE FLOOR AND SIX BOOTHS...

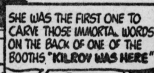

SHE WAS THE FIRST ONE TO CARVE THOSE IMMORTAL WORDS ON THE BACK OF ONE OF THE BOOTHS "KILROY WAS HERE"

ACTUALLY, ALTHOUGH GRANDMA WAS A LOT OF FUN, SHE WASN'T VERY CREATIVE!

AND SO, WORLD WAR II CAME TO AN END...

MY GRANDMOTHER LEFT HER JOB IN THE DEFENSE PLANT, AND WENT TO WORK FOR THE TELEPHONE COMPANY...

WE NEED TO STUDY THE LIVES OF GREAT WOMEN LIKE MY GRANDMOTHER... TALK TO YOUR OWN GRANDMOTHER TODAY... ASK HER QUESTIONS...

YOU'LL FIND SHE KNOWS MORE THAN PEANUT BUTTER COOKIES! THANK YOU!

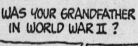

MORE FUN WITH PEANUTS FROM CORONET

CHARLES M. SCHULZ

All these books are available at your local bookshop or newsagent, or can be ordered direct from the publisher. Just tick the titles you want and fill in the form below.

Prices and availability subject to change without notice.

CORONET BOOKS, P.O. Box 11, Falmouth, Cornwall.

Please send cheque or postal order, and allow the following for postage and packing:

U.K. – 40p for one book, plus 18p for the second book, and 13p for each additional book ordered up to a £1.49 maximum.

B.F.P.O. and EIRE – 40p for the first book, plus 18p for the second book, and 13p per copy for the next 7 books, 7p per book thereafter.

OTHER OVERSEAS CUSTOMERS – 60p for the first book, plus 18p per copy for each additional book.

Name ....

Address..

....